THE RED SEA
underwater paradise

WHITE STAR PUBLISHERS

THE RED SEA
underwater paradise

Text
Angelo Mojetta

Editorial production
Valeria Manferto De Fabianis

Graphic design
Paola Piacco

Illustrations of the fish
Monica Falcone

Translations
Antony Shugaar

CONTENTS

© 2005 White Star S.p.a.
Via Candido Sassone, 22-24
13100 Vercelli, Italy
www.whitestar.it

ISBN 88-544-0094-7

Reprints:
1 2 3 4 5 6   09 08 07 06 05

Printed in China

Cover
A school of Anthias peacefully swims by a big red soft coral just out of Sharm el Sheik's coast.
Fotografia di
Claudio Cangini

Back cover
Starfish (Fromia sp.)
Fotografia di
Franco Banfi

1 Colorful colonies of soft coral (Dendronephthya sp.).

2 Blackside hawkfish (Parcirrhites forsteri).

3 Twobar anemonefish (Amphiprion bicinctus).

AN OCEAN CALLED THE RED SEA

4 Glassfish
(Parapriacanthus
guentheri) among
soft corals
(Dendronephthya
sp.).

5 Gorgonians
and soft corals
belonging to
various genera
(Dendronephthya,
Xenia,
Heteroxenia) settle
in the colonies of
dead madrepores.

Set between the African and Arabian tectonic plates, the Red Sea is the result of their slow but inexorable separation, triggered by the formation of a new sea floor, as a result of the continuous flow of molten material along the ridge that runs down the middle of this sea. For this reason, the Red Sea — aside from being a branch of the Indian Ocean, is considered by geologists to be a genuine, full-fledged ocean in formation. It is expected that, if the phenomena now underway continue with the same intensity, in about one hundred fifty million years, the Red Sea could become as vast as the Atlantic Ocean. The depression of the Red Sea extends more than 2,250 kilometers but only a little more than 1,900 kilometers, of its length is covered with water. To the north, it is blocked off by the Sinai Peninsula, which separates the gulfs of Suez and Aqaba. The Gulf of Suez, which is relatively shallow (about 90 meters at its deepest) and has a relatively flat floor, is about 250 kilometers in length, and is 32 kilometers across. The Gulf of Aqaba, 150 kilometers in length, and quite narrow, 16 kilometers across is instead far deeper, with two

depressions to the north and south, respectively 1,100 and 1,420 meters in depth. The deepest part of the Gulf of Aqaba is found along the eastern coastline, and is more than 1,800 meters. This measurement, if taken in absolute terms, seems even more impressive since the coastline in this area is surrounded by mountains that rise to elevations of over 1,500 meters. The Red Sea itself, widens out to reach a maximum width of 354 kilometers on a line with Massawa. From there it narrows gradually southward, until it is just 26 kilometers at the Strait of Bab el-Mandab, which then feeds into the Indian Ocean. As for a categorization of the sea floors in the Red Sea, it is possible to distinguish three separate physiographic regions: a coastal region that is as much as 500 meters in depth; an intermediate region of exceedingly irregular configuration, whose lower limit can be set at approximately 1,100 meters; and a deeper region running along the central axis of the Red Sea, where depths can reach as far as 1,500 to 2,000 meters. Of these three ranges, certainly the most interesting for divers is the first and shallowest. In this range, on sea

floors ranging from the surface to 50 meters in depth (just over a fifth of the total area), one will find the coral reefs, more varied and abundant in the central and northern sections of the Red Sea. Because of their characteristics, they can be considered to be a separate whole. The coral reefs found along the coastal range, both to the east and west, belong to the category of fringing reefs, and range in width from a few meters to about a kilometer. Their summits often break the waves at low tide. These coral formations develop atop a rocky sea floor or very compact detritus of organic origin, and they tend to develop lengthwise, out toward the open waters, where the better environmental conditions permit more unhindered growth of the coral polyps. This in turn leads to a progressive expansion of the reef toward the open water, and to the formation of broad channels running parallel to the shoreline; in some cases, and especially in the southern section of the sea and along the Sudanese coasts, these channels can become so broad that they begin to resemble lagoons. The fringing reef, finally, presents another distinctive characteristic.

As one can see from an aerial photograph or from a detailed nautical chart, the reefs are broken occasionally — generally in correspondence with valleys that open out in the mainland — by narrow channels that are extensions of the beds of ancient rivers or the course of temporary rivers that form during the rainy seasons. Depending on the location, these channels, which hover in delicate equilibrium between the growth and the erosion of the coral, take the name of *marsa* or *sharm*. The fringing reefs, however, are not the only coral formations in the Red Sea. Off the coasts of Egypt, Sudan, and Saudi Arabia, on a line with ancient rocky sea floors, which had once emerged from the water because of a decline in the sea level, there are colonies of coral whose continual growth has kept steady pace with the rising sea level, resulting in the appearance of both coral islands and true barrier reefs, several kilometers in length, and surrounded by sea floors that drop sharply away to depths ranging from 500 to 800 meters. Despite the fact that the presence of corals is certainly one of the greatest attractions of this sea, they should still be considered

— at least in certain areas — as an anomaly. The Red Sea, in fact, extends far to the north (as far as 30° N. latitude), and into latitudes where the climatic conditions usually prevent the growth of these organisms, capable of surviving only in waters where the temperature never drops below 10° C. The Red Sea, on the other hand, being a closed body of water, is unusually hot, and there are minimum temperatures (in February) of around 20-22° C in the northern section and around 27° C in the southern and central basin. The peak temperatures, on the other hand, oscillate around 30-32° C, although in coastal areas with very shallow sea beds and enclosed bays, the temperature can rise as high as 45° C. As for the salinity, the scanty rainfall (just 180 millimeters a year in the area considered rainiest: the region of Suakin), and the very high atmospheric temperatures, which increase evaporation, and the limited water-exchange with the neighboring seas, all help to raise these levels to 38-40 per thousand (i.e., 38-40 grams of salt in every liter of water) with high points that can go to as much as 45-50 per thousand.

STRUCTURE AND MAKE-UP OF CORAL REEFS

*6 Ras
Mohammad, Sinai's
southernmost
cape.*

*7 Soft corals
(Dendronephthya
sp.).*

Coral reefs are immense formations, as hard as rock; only the external section of the reef is actually alive. With a very slow rate of growth, on average about a centimeter per year, though of course there are exceptions, these formations are the result of the incessant growth of living organisms, generally known as corals, even though the technical term would be madrepores. Constituted by a living part equipped with numerous tentacles, the polyp, and by a limestone cup-shaped section, the corallite, the corals with which a scuba diver comes into contact during his time underwater are organisms that live in colonies that may vary considerably in shape and size. They are distinguished by a rigid skeleton made up of calcium carbonate and other mineral salts drawn from the sea water through the specific metabolism of these animals. In the Red Sea, specialists have identified more than 170 different species of corals; clearly it is impossible to condense a complete description of them into a few pages. The most common genera are the *Acropora* and *Montipora*, to which we might well add the *Fungia*, *Porites*, *Favia*, *Favites*, *Stylophora*, *Pavona*, *Leptoseris*, and *Cycloseris*. The distribution of the various species is mainly regulated by the environmental conditions (transparency, depths, and hydrodynamics of the water), so that it soon becomes possible to recognize, within certain limits, the existence of preferred areas for one or the other type of coral formation and the recurrence of certain associations of species. And so, if we imagine a dive beginning near the shore and proceeding toward open waters along the reef, we will first find colonies of *Stylophora* (family *Pocipolloridae*). These are ramified colonies with large corallites. The ramifications, slightly compressed and more-or-less flattened at the tips, are light-brown in color, while the extremities of the branches are pink or purple, and the tips are white. Proceeding toward the open sea, we shall encounter colonies of *Favia*, *Favites*, and *Porites*. The first two genera mentioned can be recognized by their massive colonies, rounded or columnar, or else encrusting (in deep water) and especially for the orderly appearance of their corallites, which look like the honeycomb cells of a beehive (infact, their name comes from the Latin for "hive," in fact). This is their most distinctive feature, while their colors, ranging from whitish to a more-or-less intense pinkish hue, and size (depending upon the age of the colony, as is the case with all corals) are exceedingly variable. The genus *Porites*, which is

among the most common, is a
bellwether of sheltered waters with
sandy floors. These are large
colonies generally rounded in shape,
with minute corallites; they resemble
compact masses of rock, and are
light brown in color. The outermost
and most exposed areas of reef,
lastly, are dominated by the genus
Acropora, whose species (15 in the
Red Sea) can be considered to be
madrepores par excellence. They
generally form ramifying colonies,
described as "staghorn corals,"
which are quite common in the first
10 meters of the reef overlooking
the open waters. At greater depths,
on the other hand, the *Acropora* tend
to expand, forming platform-shaped,
or umbrella-shaped colonies, with
broad flat surfaces supported by a
columnar base. Alongside the hard
corals, there are other colonial
organisms, such as the gorgonians
and soft corals, whose shapes and
colors are main attractions to the
underwater photographers who dive

along the reefs of the Red Sea in
search of startling and captivating
pictures. In reference to the former,
we might point out that they have a
corneous skeleton, hard but elastic,
which tends to form perpendicular
to the current above rocky sea beds,
especially in the more exposed and
less well lit sections of the reef.
A number of gorgonians, known as
sea whips because they do not have
the usual tree-like branching shape,
resemble long stalks, distinguished
by a little curl or burr at the end.
In the Red Sea, the Gorgonacea are
not particularly abundant while,
on the contrary, the soft corals,
or Alcyonacea are quite common.
The texture of the latter is quite soft
or rubbery to the touch, because
the limestone component, though it
exists, is limited to thin spicules
incorporated in the main supporting
tissues. These spicules can be clearly
seen in the species of the genus
Dendronephthya, which are among
the most common and the loveliest

in the Red Sea, due to their
arborescent, or ramifying,
appearance. There translucent and
brightly colored Alcyonacea (fuchsia,
pink, or orange) have their polyps
clustered together, not unlike the
cauliflower-like inflorescences,
supported by branches that develop
along a single plane or in many
directions. These are carnivorous
organisms, just like the gorgonians
and the hard corals, and for that
reason it is more common to see
them in an expanded form during the
night, when they double or even
triple their size; in the case of
Dendronephthya klunzingeri they
can become more than a meter in
height. The soft corals are more
common in the upper 15 meters from
the surface, where there are more-
or-less encrusting species, which at
a first glance are reminiscent of large
actinia with short but numerous
tentacles, or formations of moss
that at times can cover many
square meters of the sea bottom.

THE FISH OF THE RED SEA

Since the Red Sea is a branch of the Indian Ocean, its fish life naturally displays considerable affinities with the fish found in the neighboring ocean, even though the geological history of this sea, which begins about 40 million years ago, has led to the evolution of many endemic species; the latter constitute about 17 percent of the thousand and more species that inhabit the Red Sea.

The chief cause of the abundance of life on the coral sea beds is the remarkable fertility of this environment, which is as varied and complex as its inhabitants. The reefs of the Red Sea, which are always changing, craggy, and broken by underwater crevices and fissures, dotted with pillar, mushroom, or umbrella formations that mark off the sands or the underwater pastures; these formations provide an infinite array of habitats to sea creatures. Some find this area to be a perfect haven in which to elude the pursuit of predators; others lurk there in ambush, or hide their eggs or their young, or they establish peculiar inter-species

relationships, like those between clownfish and the sea anemones, the cardinal fish *(Paramia sp., Apogon sp.)* and the black sea urchins, or to name another still, that between the gobies and the crayfish of the genus *Alpheus*, the two creatures comfortably sharing the same underwater den. All of these reef-dwelling creatures find food there, be that constituted by other fish, plankton, algae, coral polyps, detritus, or other forms of nourishment.

The coral reef varies in more aspects than just the shapes and the seascape. There are also gradients of differentiation, linked to the depth, with such varying factors as hydrodynamics, luminosity, and temperature. Each of these parameters, in the final analysis, affects others still, in accordance with mechanisms whose ultimate product is the abundance of life mentioned here so frequently.

As a result, in just a few ten square meters of reef, one might find hundreds of fish, belonging to dozens of different species, and yet living in perfect harmony, to mention the numerous invertebrates. Only a great number of dives can make a diver familiar with the many different sets of relationships between fish and environment. Inevitably, however, the clearest set of relationships will be those linked to the variety of colors displayed. Even though the colors of the fishes are so exceedingly evident to the eyes of humans, they are not equally evident to the eyes of their fellow fish and even, in many cases, serve to conceal or to camouflage them.

For example, the common ocellate blotches found near the tail or on the dorsal fin, and the dark bands that often cover the eyes, are there to confuse attacking predators, who take the blotches for the real eyes, often attacking the intended prey in sections of the body that are not as vital as expected.

Likewise, the garish colorings made up of blotches or stripes of

8 Sea fan gorgonian (Subergorgia hicksoni).

9 Humphead wrasse (Cheilinus undulatus).

10-11 Grey reef shark (Carcharhinus amblyrhynchos).

contrasting colors, which appear to human eyes as if they were neon advertising signs, actually serve to confuse the fish's outline, breaking it up into many different tiles, or to blend it in with the welter of coral branches or in the lacy patchwork structure of the gorgonians.

But the colorings are not only deceptive in function.

Indeed, in some cases they are used to transmit very specific messages. The groupers, for example, can rapidly change their coloring, accordingly with whether they feel threatened, fearful, or are sleeping and therefore feel tranquil and calm. Indeed, marine biologists have coined the term "pajama coloring" to indicate the markings that certain fishes take on during their nightly repose; these nocturnal markings can be so different from the diurnal colorings that one may think that these are two different species. In other cases, especially among the Labrids or the parrotfish, the coloring makes it fairly easy to recognize specimens of one gender or the other, or the degree of maturity. And in many species of fish, the difference in color between adults and the young prevents useless battles between species. Lastly, there are colorings that transmit explicit messages, such as: "I am ready for mating," "I am dangerous," or "I am completely inedible."

Equally varied are the forms that the many different fish can take on. Before the eyes of the diver, float, dart, and hover fish of serpentine shape (morays, needle fish, cornet fish), tapered form (groupers, wrasse, tuna, and jacks), globular (globe fish) or else flattened or compressed (angelfish, butterfly fish, surgeon fish, trigger fish) or depressed (rays, eagle-rays, manta rays). To a careful observer, each different shape is clearly linked to the habits of each species and the type of environment in which it lives. This is shown by the fact that coral reefs dominated by a few species of corals, therefore

with little variation, are home to a great number of fish belonging to relatively few species.

The various colonies of corals often house specific populations of small fish. The banded dascyllus *(Dascyllus aruanus)* establishes its territory among the branches of the *Pocillopora* and the *Acropora*.

The latter are also home to populations of blue-green chromis *(Chromis caerulea)* or half-and-half chromis *(C. dimidiata)* along with young specimens of jacks, trigger fish, and boxfish. Of particular interest to an underwater photographer is the umbrella-shaped formation of the *Acropora*; in their shelter one can find angelfish, butterflyfish, surgeonfish, and grunts, while the sands at the base of these formations are often home to blue-spotted lagoon rays *(Taeniura lymma)*.

The part of the coral reef that is most abundant in life, however, remains the outer area, which is also frequented by larger fishes, such as sharks.

About thirty different species of shark live in the Red Sea, but the two most common are the white-tip reef shark *(Triaenodon obesus* and the black-tip reef shark *(Carcharhinus melanopterus)*.

In deeper waters, ranging from 10 to 50 meters it is also possible to encounter *Carcharhinus albimarginatus, C. plumbeus* or *C. wheeleri*, while in grottoes and under some coral formations it is possible to find nurse shark *(Nebrius ferrugineus)*.

Rare, but far more dangerous, are the tiger shark *(Galeocerdo cuvieri)*, the mako *(Isurus glaucus)*, and the hammerhead shark *(Sphyrna sp.)*.

Fascinating and harmless are the eagle ray *(Aetobatus narinari)*, their backs spotted with white, the manta ray *(Manta birostris)* which can attain a width of 5 meters and the devilfish *(Mobula diabolus)*. Among the larger predators that appear suddenly from the open sea we should mention the barracuda *(Sphyraena barracuda,*

Sphyraena qenie) jacks *(Caranx melampygus, C. sexfasciatus, C. ignobilis)*, easy to recognize because of the deeply cleft, forked tail, and the sharply marked lateral line. Mingling with them are often large humphead wrasse *(Cheilinus undulatus)*, parrotfish, unicornfish, and swarms of colorful fusiliers *(Caesio sp.)*.

Although a dive in tropical seas is a fascinating experience one

should not forget that a coral reef conceals dangers that can be harmful and even fatal, especially if one is ignorant of them.

A number of dangerous or potentially dangerous creatures, such as sharks, barracuda, morays, and scorpionfish, are well known, but they are not the only ones. A more detailed, and very useful, list, should include the stonefish, both true *(Synanceia verrucosa)* and false *(Scorpaenopsis diabolus)*, dangerous because of their potentially venomous spines, and especially because of their camouflaged coloration, which makes them hard to see.

Equally dangerous though little known are the so-called fire corals *(Millepora dichotoma, M. platyphylla)* which are equipped with powerful stinging cells capable of producing "burns" which should receive immediate care, since they can easily become infected; the mollusks of the genus *Conus*, capable of launching small, poisonous darts; sea urchins, both the long-spined *Diadema* and the *Astenosoma*, whose bright red or green coloring may well attract a diver — caution is the watchword, because the short white- and red-tipped spines are quite venomous.

SHARKS, RAYS, MANTA RAYS, AND EAGLE RAYS: THE GREAT CARTILAGINOUS FISH

BARRACUDAS AND CARANGIDS: PREDATORS OF HIGH SEAS

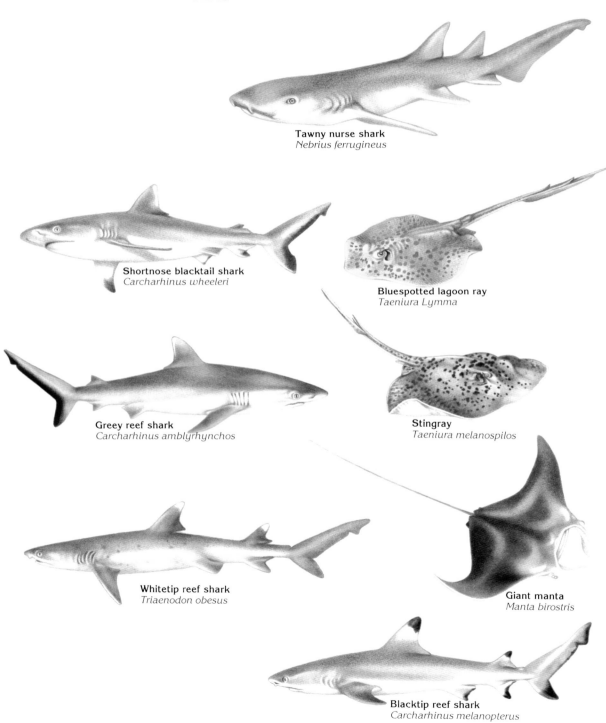

Tawny nurse shark
Nebrius ferrugineus

Shortnose blacktail shark
Carcharhinus wheeleri

Bluespotted lagoon ray
Taeniura Lymma

Greey reef shark
Carcharhinus amblyrhynchos

Stingray
Taeniura melanospilos

Whitetip reef shark
Triaenodon obesus

Giant manta
Manta birostris

Blacktip reef shark
Carcharhinus melanopterus

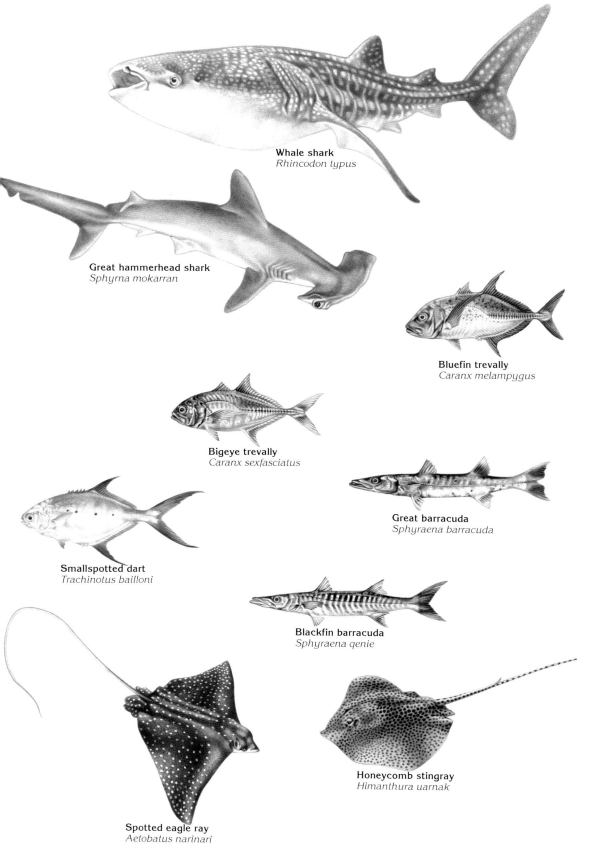

Whale shark
Rhincodon typus

Great hammerhead shark
Sphyrna mokarran

Bluefin trevally
Caranx melampygus

Bigeye trevally
Caranx sexfasciatus

Great barracuda
Sphyraena barracuda

Smallspotted dart
Trachinotus bailloni

Blackfin barracuda
Sphyraena qenie

Honeycomb stingray
Himanthura uarnak

Spotted eagle ray
Aetobatus narinari

13

14-15
Whale shark
(Rhincodon
typus).

Intriguing and far less dangerous than is still commonly believed, sharks are frequent visitors to the reefs of the Red Sea. Endowed with a cartilaginous skeleton, and not a bony one like those of the other fish, and without a swimming bladder — which means that many sharks are forced to swim incessantly in order to maintain the desired depth — sharks are tapered and hydrodynamic in shape, made particularly distinctive by the tailfin with the larger upper lobe. The shortnose blacktail shark and the blacktip reef shark *(Carcharhinus wheeleri, C. melanopterus)*, the whitetip reef shark *(Triaenodon obesus)*, and the tawny nurse shark *(Nebrius ferrugineus)* are among the sharks most frequently encountered along the coral reefs, but while the first two swim tirelessly, appearing and vanishing from the view of the scuba divers, the whitetip reef shark and the tawny nurse shark are easy to watch, as they lie resting during the day in their underwater grottoes. Rarer, but not impossible to spot, are the oceanic whitetip sharks *(C. longimanus)*, the hammerhead shark *(Sphyrna sp.)*, and the whale shark *(Rhincodon typus)*, which is gigantic (more than 12 meters in length), but entirely harmless.

14 bottom
Great hammerhead
(Sphyrna
mokarran).

15 Tawny
nurse shark
(Nebrius
ferrugineus).

16 top
Whitetip reef shark
(Triaenodon
obesus).

16 center
Oceanic
whitetip shark
(Carcharhinus
longimanus).

16 bottom and 16-17
Shortnose
blacktail shark
(Carcharhinus
wheeleri).

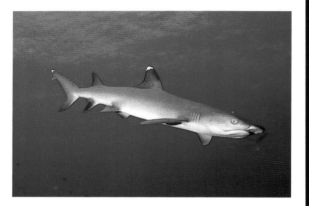

Cartilaginous fish like the sharks, but entirely different in shape due to an evolutionary history that led them to live on the ocean floor, are the great rays (the bluespotted lagoon ray and the Honeycomb stingray, or *Taeniura lymma* and *Himanthura uarnak*), often found on sandy expanses where they lie poised like airplanes ready for takeoff. Belonging to the same order (Raiformes) are the spotted eaglerays *(Aetobatus narinari)*, with their great pointy pectoral fins and long tails, and the enormous, majestic giant mantas *(Manta birostris)*, black and white in color, with fins that attain a width of 5 to 6 meters, marked by their two cephalic fins shaped like mitts, which they use to convey food toward their mouths.

18-19
Spotted eagle ray
(Aetobatus
narinari).

18 bottom
Bluespotted
lagoon ray
(Taeniura lymma).

19 top
School of spotted
eagle ray
(Aetobatus
narinari).

19 bottom
Giant manta
(Manta birostris).

Sharing their habits as predatory fish that live along the boundary between the reef and the open sea, barracudas *(Sphyraena sp.)* and carangids (the bluefin trevally and the bigeye trevally, or *Caranx melampygus* and *C. sexfasciatus*) move in schools that can number dozens and dozens of specimens, in search of their habitual prey, which include the smaller schoolfish; they attack these smaller fish after herding them toward the reef so as to hinder their escape. Barracudas are considered to be potentially dangerous to humans, but in reality the very few attacks on record, with expert verification, have proven to occur in murky waters, and to have involved particularly large and solitary barracudas, or else barracudas that were attacked or disturbed by a scuba diver.

20 top
Yellowspotted jack
(Carangoides bajad).

20 center
Silver Pompano
(Trachinotus blochii).

20 bottom
Bigeye jack
(Caranx sexfasciatus).

21 top
Bluefin trevally
(Caranx melampygus).

20-21
Blackfin barracuda
(Sphyraena qenie).

BETWEEN DENS AND GROTTOES

Undulated moray
Gymnothorax undulatus

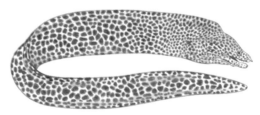

Grey moray
Siderea grisea

Honeycomb moray
Gymnothorax favagineus

Giant moray
Gymnothorax javanicus

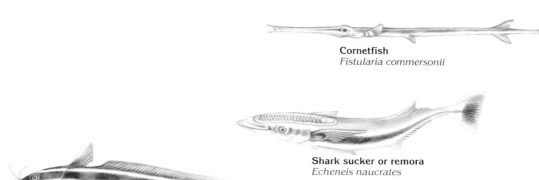

Cornetfish
Fistularia commersonii

Shark sucker or remora
Echeneis naucrates

Striped eel catfish
Plotosus lineatus

22-23
Giant moray
(Gymnothorax
javanicus).

Elongated in shape, sinuous, and similar to snakes —
except for the remora — the fish described on these
pages are typical sea bed dwellers and feeders.
The morays (e.g., the grey moray and the giant moray,
respectively *Siderea grisea* and *Gymnothorax javanicus*)
are commonly encountered amidst the crannies of the
reefs. There are numerous underwater grottoes and
crannies that these animals choose as their refuge
during the day; from the entrances of these cavities,
they extend their open mouths showing their powerful
front teeth in a display that seems threatening but, in
fact, is not. The morays keep their mouths agape
because this is their way of breathing.

24 top
Grey moray
(Siderea grisea).

24 bottom
Hundulated
moray young
(Gymnothorax
undulatus).

25 top left
Spotted garden eel
(Heteroconger
hassi).

25 top right
Remora
(Echeneis
naucrates).

25 bottom
Cornetfish
(Fistularia
commersonii).

Much cannier and more cunning are the so-called garden eels, a term which refers to their odd life-style. These fish *(Heteroconger hassi)* live in very sizable groups on the sandy sea floors, where each one digs its own den, with part of their bodies protruding, though they never entirely leave the little tunnel that they have dug in the sand.

From a distance, it is possible to see dozens and dozens of these creatures undulating in the water, but one need only get a few meters closer, and the eels will vanish in a flash.

Elongated in shape, but with a narrow tubular snout that ends in a pair of thick lips, the cornetfish *(Fistularia commersonii)* move slowly and rigidly through the water, counting on their innocuous appearance and especially on their uniform coloring, to venture quite close to smaller fish, who are then literally sucked into the cornetfish's large mouth. Perfectly evolved to hitch rides upon larger fish, and therefore exceedingly difficult to spot on their own, remoras *(Echeneis naucrates)* are constant companions of sharks and mantas, to whose bodies they fasten by virtue of having the anterior dorsal fin converted into an oval transversely lamellate suctorial disc on the top of the head, by means of which they adhere firmly.

THE QUEENS OF THE SEA BED: GROUPERS

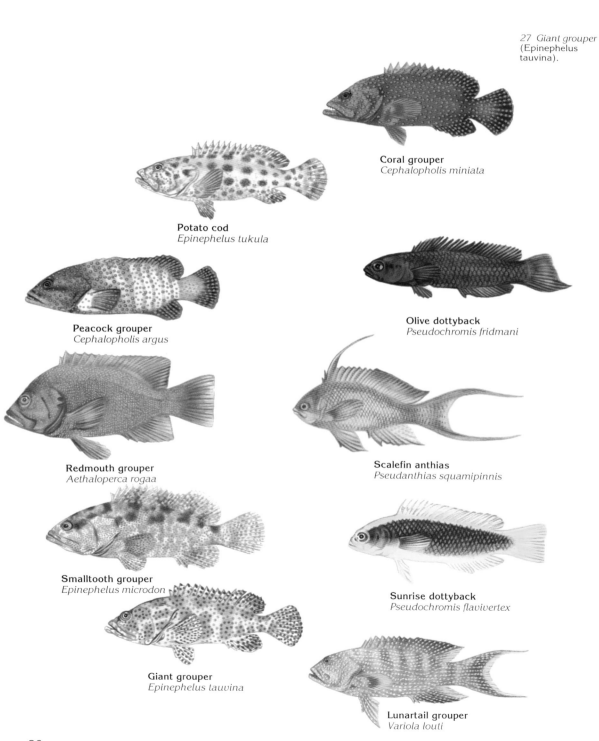

27 Giant grouper (Epinephelus tauvina).

Coral grouper
Cephalopholis miniata

Potato cod
Epinephelus tukula

Olive dottyback
Pseudochromis fridmani

Peacock grouper
Cephalopholis argus

Redmouth grouper
Aethaloperca rogaa

Scalefin anthias
Pseudanthias squamipinnis

Smalltooth grouper
Epinephelus microdon

Sunrise dottyback
Pseudochromis flavivertex

Giant grouper
Epinephelus tauvina

Lunartail grouper
Variola louti

Among the fish most commonly found on coral reefs, ranging from depths of just a few meters to well beyond the limits to which a scuba diver can safely venture, one will certainly find groupers, almost all of them distinctive for their lively colors, powerful bodies, broad tailfins, and large mouths, with the lower jaw larger than the upper. The considerable variety of environments that one can encounter during a dive along the coral reefs of the Red Sea explains the great number of species of groupers that one can observe. There are small colorful groupers, such as the coral grouper (Cephalopholis miniata) and the peacock grouper (C. argus), there are mid-sized groupers such as the lunartail grouper (Variola louti), distinguished by a caudal fin shaped like a crescent or sickle, that is unique among the groupers, and the redmouth grouper (Aethaloperca rogaa) all the way up to the giants of the group, such as Epinephelus tukula, the potato cod, which can grow to be as long as two meters. Although some species are more frequent by day, others at dawn or sunset, and still others by night, groupers all have territorial habits (each one lives in a den where it spends much of its time and where it takes refuge if it is disturbed) and are all carnivorous, feeding on fish, crustaceans, and octopuses.

28-29
Coral grouper
(Cephalopholis
miniata).

29 top
Giant grouper
(Epinephelus
tauvina).

29 bottom
Potato cod
(Epinephelus
tukula).

*30 top
Lunartail grouper
(Variola louti).*

*30-31
Peacock grouper
(Cephalopholis
argus).*

*31 top Red Sea
grouper
(Plectropomus p.
marisrubri).*

The orange clouds of color and life that surround the more extensive and jagged coral formations, on the other hand, are made up of little fish belonging to the same family as the grouper, the Serranidae.
These little fish are scalefin anthias *(Pseudanthias squamipinnis)*, which attain lengths of up to 15 centimeters; they live in isolated groups, each one near a coral formation. Oddly enough, each group could more accurately be described as a harem, inasmuch as there is a dominant male surrounded by females.

The males are distinguished by their brighter coloring, but especially by the long ray set in the first section of the anterior fin. Since these fish change sex as they mature, upon the death of the male, the largest female assumes the dominant role. The coral nooks and fissures are home to other small fish with a shape more tapered than the scalefin anthias; these splendid fish are spectacularly colorful, such as the olive dottyback, or *Pseudochromis fridmani*, with its fluorescent violet hue, which is found only in the Red

33 top
Jewel fairy basslet
male
(Pseudanthias
squamipinnis).

33 center
Jewel fairy basslet
female
(Pseudanthias
squamipinnis).

33 bottom
Olive dottyback
(Pseudochromis
fridmani).

32-33
Scalefin anthias
female
(Pseudanthias
squamipinnis).

THE FISH OF THE NIGHT

Crown squirrelfish
Sargocentron diadema

Blotcheye soldierfish
Myripristis murdjan

Sabre squirrelfish
Sargocentron spiniferum

Vanikoro sweeper
Pempheris vanicolensis

Golden cardinalfish
Apogon aureus

Goggle eye
Priacanthus hamrur

Flash light fish
Photoblepharon palpebratus

*35
Sabre squirrelfish
(Sargocentron
spiniferum).*

At the mouths of underwater grottoes or inside those grottoes, it is possible to observe a number of fish during the day that are linked by their coloring, based on red, and by their large eyes. They are not very active, and lie practically motionless under the gaze of the scuba diver, giving the impression that they are imprisoned in a glass display case. In reality, these fish (squirrelfish, soldierfish, cardinalfish, and Priacanthidae belong, respectively, to the genera *Sargocentron, Myripristis, Apogon,* and *Priacanthus*) are nocturnal and evening species, who dislike bright light and therefore take refuge in the underwater grottoes or in the less brightly lit areas; they emerge at nightfall to take the place of the diurnal fish, so that life on the reef never slows down.

36 top and 36-37
Goggle eye
(Priacanthus hamrur).

36 bottom
Sabre squirrelfish
(Sargocentron
spiniferum).

38-39
Glass fish
(Parapriacanthus
guentheri).

38 bottom
Lyretail hogfish
young
(Bodianus
anthioides).

Equally fearful of light are the Pempheridae, small fish *(Pempheris vanicolensis)* that loiter in large schools in the shadier areas, where they remain until sunset, when they scatter away across the reef, just like the other fish described here, in search of food. These are commonly known to scuba divers as "glassfish" because of their glittering coloration, which reflects the light of the photographer's flashgun like a many-faceted mirror.

39 top
Vanikoro sweeper
(Pempheris
vanicolensis).

39 bottom
Glass fish
(Parapriacanthus
guentheri).

Fashinating but dangerous

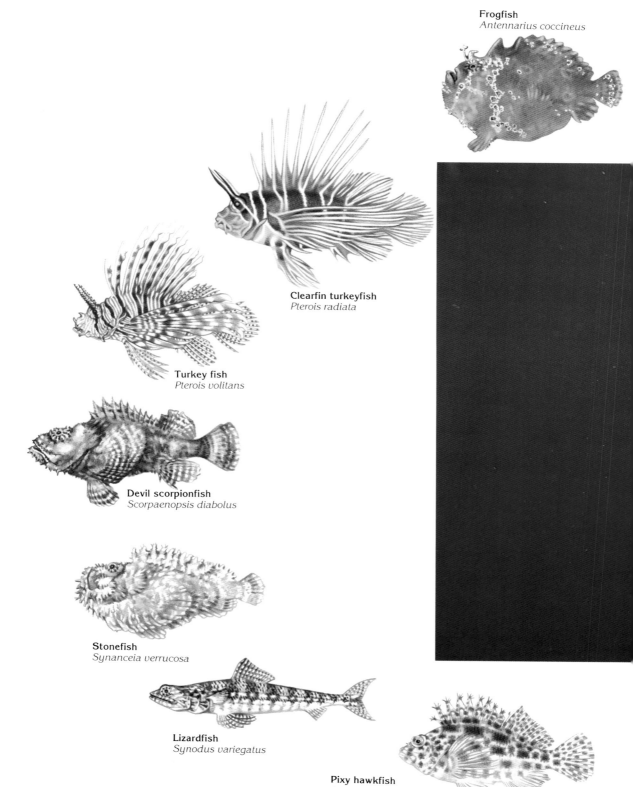

Frogfish
Antennarius coccineus

Clearfin turkeyfish
Pterois radiata

Turkey fish
Pterois volitans

Devil scorpionfish
Scorpaenopsis diabolus

Stonefish
Synanceia verrucosa

Lizardfish
Synodus variegatus

Pixy hawkfish
Cirrhitichthys oxycephalus

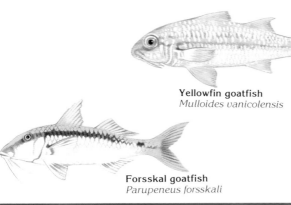

Yellowfin goatfish
Mulloides vanicolensis

Yellow saddle goatfish
Parupeneus cyclostomus

Forsskal goatfish
Parupeneus forsskali

*40-41 Turkey fish
(Pterois volitans).*

Longnose hawkfish
Oxycirrhites typus

Crocodile fish
Cociella crocodila

41

Keeping a careful eye on the sea floor over which one is swimming and on the waters around, allows alert scuba divers in the Red Sea to avoid some of the greatest menaces to which they are exposed. These dangers are the stonefish *(Synanceia verrucosa)*, truly quite similar in appearance to little pieces of rock; they can only be distinguished from actual stones by a sharp eye, capable of making out the nearly vertical profile of the mouth and the moving eyes. For that reason, it is wise to be particularly careful of how one places one's hands on the coral floors. The chief threat posed by these fish lies in their very strong spinal rays (they can even penetrate beach shoes!) linked to glands that secrete a highly toxic venom comparable to that of the most lethally venomous snakes. Equally camouflaged, but less dangerous,

42 Clearfin turkeyfish (Pterois radiata).

43 top Stonefish (Synanceia verrucosa).

43 center Scorpionfish (Scorpaenopsis barbatus).

43 bottom Filament finned stinger (Inimicus filamentosus).

are the devil scorpionfish *(Scorpaenopsis diabolus)*, similar in shape and behavior to the scorpionfish of Mediterranean waters. More elegant and lovely, but not less dangerous are the Scorpaenidae of the genus *Pterois* (turkeyfish and clearfin turkeyfish, respectively *Pterois volitans* and *P. radiata*), distinguished by their fins with long rays, similar to plumes, which actually conceal venomous spines. If carefully approached, they can be watched in peace, as long as one is certain not to corner them in situations where they might feel hemmed in or in danger, so that they might attack, their venomous spines levelled forward.

44 top
Longnose
hawkfish
(Oxycirrhites
typus).

44 bottom
Goldsaddle
goatfish
(Parupeneus
cyclostomus).

44-45
Blackside
hawkfish
(Paracirrhites
forsteri).

Surrounded by myriads of colorful fish that swim all around him, a scuba diver is likely to lose sight of the sea floor, and with it, the opportunity to observe fish that may be less chromatically attractive than others, but equally remarkable and interesting in their ways of life. Very much like the mullets of the Mediterranean Sea, the yellowsaddle goatfish and Forsskal's goatfish of the Red Sea *(Parupeneus forskali* and *P. cyclostomus)* dart along near the bottom, sampling the sediment with their long and mobile barbles, dense with sensory cells. Smaller and brightly colored, but equally well camouflaged are the longnose hawkfish *(Oxycirrhites typus)* and the blackside hawkfish *(Parracirrhites forsteri)*, which tend to perch on the sea floor or on the branches of gorgonians, where the longnose hawkfish in particular blend in by virtue of their coloring made up of white and red checks, and because of their small size (13 centimeters).

46 top
Speckled
sandperch
(Parapercis
hexophtalma).

46 bottom
Crocodile fish
(Cociella
crocodila).

46-47
Lizardfish
(Synodus
variegatus).

More difficult to see are the lizardfish and the crocodile fish. The former *(Synodus variegatus)* wait in ambush on the sea floor, where their colors camouflage them, making them look like pieces of abandoned coral. The latter *(Cociella crocodila)*, instead, with their flattened bodies and long, wide snouts, like to bury themselves among the sediment, leaving only part of their head, their eyes, and their dorsal fins protruding from the dirt.

SCHOOLFISH

Blackspotted grunt
Plectorhynchus gaterinus

Suez fusilier
Caesio suevicus

Twinspot snapper
Lutjanus bohar

Snubnose chub
Kyphosus cinerascens

Bluestripe snapper
Lutjanus kasmira

Spangled emperor
Lethrinus nebulosus

Mangrove snapper
Lutjanus argentimaculatus

Goldstriped soapfish
Grammistes sexlineatus

Humpback snapper
Lutjanus gibbus

Thumbprint emperor
Lethrinus harak

These species of fish swimming amongst the corals
and amidst the reefs astonish observers with their
frequently colorful markings (for example, the fusiliers
of the genus *Caesio*, the Haemulidae, such as the
blackspotted grunt or sweetlips, *Plectorhynchus
gaterinus*) and with their remarkable size, which can
reach lengths of more than 55 or 60 centimeters
(twinspot snapper, or *Lutjanus bohar*). In part,
predators, and in part, plankton-eaters, whether
diurnal or nocturnal, these species indicate by their
mere presence the areas richest in food, and are
among the first — especially the larger Lutjanidae,
called snappers for a good reason to reach areas
where the larger predators have just finished fighting
over prey, eager to snap up a bit of the leftovers.

54-55
Striped butterflyfish
(Chaetodon
fasciatus).

55 top
Threadfin butterflyfish
(Chaetodon auriga).

55 center
Crown butterflyfish
(Chaetodon
paucifasciatus).

55 bottom
Lined butterflyfish
(Chaetodon
lineolatus).

Among the most distinctive of the species found in these families, we should mention the masked butterflyfish *(Chaetodon semilarvatus)* which is often found in schools, the crown butterflyfish *(C. paucifasciatus)*, the schooling bannerfish *(Heniochus intermedius)*, the Arabian angelfish *(Pomacanthus asfur)*, dark blue, with a broad yellow band extending from the belly to the back. Flattened, tall bodies are also found in the batfish *(Platax orbicularis)* which measure as much as 50 or 60 centimeters in length, and nearly the same in height, so that they resemble disks, especially the adults.

56 top left and 57
Royal angelfish
(Pygoliptes
diacanthus).

56 top right
Yellowbar angelfish
(Pomacanthus
maculosus).

56 bottom left
Emperor angelfish
(Pomacanthus
imperator).

56 bottom right
Arabian angelfish
(Pomacanthus
asfur).

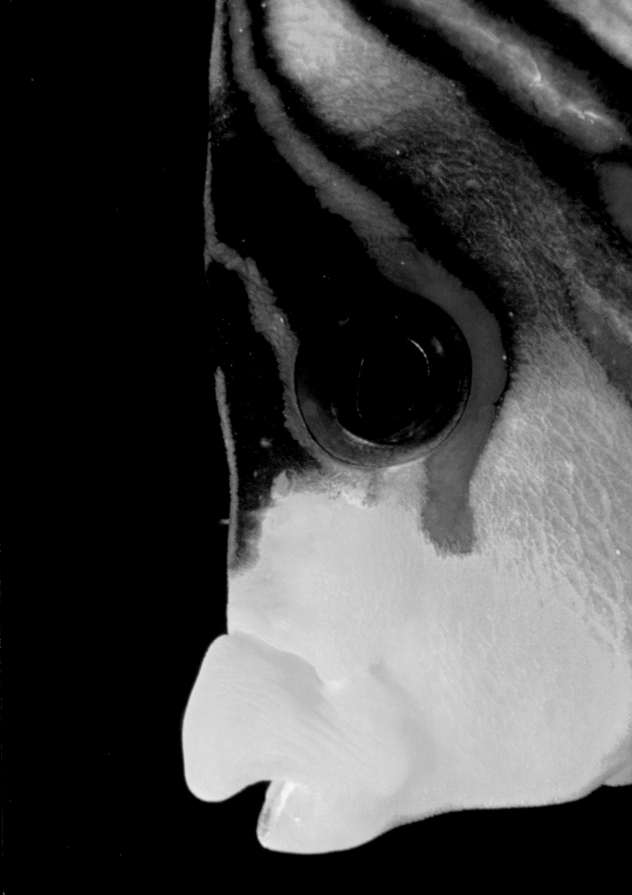

59 top
Red Sea bannerfish
(Heniochus
diphreutes).

59 center
Masked
butterflyfish
(Chaetodon
semilarvatus).

59 bottom
Masked
butterflyfish
(Chaetodon
semilarvatus) and
schooling
bannerfish
(Heniochus
diphreutes)

58 Red Sea
bannerfish
(Heniochus
intermedius).

SMALL, CAMOUFLAGED, AND ODDLY BEHAVED

Banded dascyllus
Dascyllus aruanus

Domino damselfish
Dascyllus trimaculatus

Twobar anemonefish
Amphiprion bicinctus

Sixspot goby
Valenciennea sexguttata

Half-and-half chromis
Chromis dimidiata

Sulphur damselfish
Pomacentrus sulfureus

Sergeant major
Abudefduf saxatilis

Mimic blenny
Aspidontus taeniatus

Sergeant scissortail
Abudefduf sexfasciatus

Blue-green chromis
Chromis viridis

61 Whipcoral dwarfgoby (Bryaninops youngei).

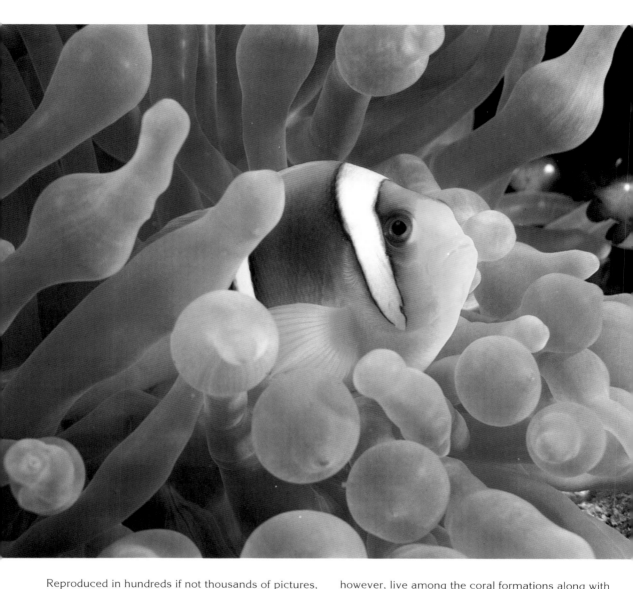

Reproduced in hundreds if not thousands of pictures, the Pomacentridae are fundamentally represented by the clownfish *(Amphiprion sp.)* which, due to their characteristics, are considered a group to themselves. Despite the fact that they are so widely known, they still never fail to attract the attention of scuba divers, especially if those divers are also underwater photographers, due to their odd habit of living in close proximity to the stinging sea anemones, which constitute an impregnable defense against would-be predators. Often scuba divers have a chance to observe the female caring for the eggs laid at the base of the anemones, helped by the male who intently wards off intruders with the remarkable aggressivity that so contrasts with the usual behavior of the little clownfish. Along with the *Amphiprion*, one can often observe small black fish with three white spots. These are the young of the domino damselfish *(Dascyllus trimaculatus)*, the adults of which,

however, live among the coral formations along with dozens of other specimens belonging to countlesss species of damselfish, such as the banded dascyllus *(Dascyllus aruanus)*, the bluegreen chromis, and the half-and-half chromis (respectively, *Chromis caerulea* and *C. dimidiata*), entirely similar to their counterparts in the Mediterranean. Larger and unmistakable due to their coloring in broad white and black bands are the sergeant major and the sergeant scissortail (respectively, *Abudefduf saxatilis* and *A. sexfasciatus*) which gather in great closely packed groups in the water, surrounding and following scuba divers, without fear. Smaller, and generally found on the sea floor, in the countless nooks and crannies of the corals, are the Blennidae, or blennies, many of which have distinctive barbs or fringed filaments on their heads, and the Gobiidae, or gobies, with short snouts and ventral fins transformed into suctorial disks with which they adhere to the sea beds.

62-63
Twobar
anemonefish
(Amphiprion
bicinctus).

63 top
Sergeant major
(Abudefduf saxatilis).

63 center
Red Sea mimic
blenny
(Ecsenius gravieri).

63 bottom
Lemon goby
(Gobiodon
citrinus).

64 top
Banded dascyllus
(Dascyllus
aruanus).

64 bottom
Domino
damselfish
(Dascyllus
trimaculatus).

64-65 Chromis
(Chromis sp.).

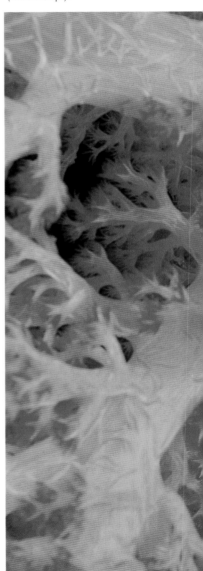

65 top
Blue-green chromis
(Chromis caerulea).

Klunzinger's w
Thalassoma klu

Abudjubbe wrasse
Cheilinus abudjubbe

Moon wrasse
Thalassoma lunare

Eightline wrasse
Paracheilinus octotaenia

African coris
Coris gaimard

Humphead wrasse
Cheilinus undulatus

Broomtail wrasse
Cheilinus lunulatus

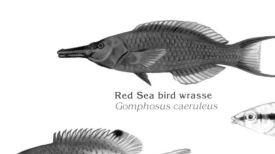

Red Sea bird wrasse
Gomphosus caeruleus

Yellowtail wrasse
Anampses meleagrides

Cleaner wrasse
Labroides dimidiatus

Axilspot hogfish
Bodianus axillaris

66-67 Klunzinger's wrasse (Thalassoma klunzingeri).

Extremely widespread, but differing radically in shape, coloring, and size, the Labridae do resemble each other in their elongated body shape, which is slightly compressed, and in the single long dorsal fin. Their way of swimming is also quite distinctive. The Labridae, in fact, swim by propelling themselves forward or backward with powerful strokes of their pectoral fins, which they use like oars; this gives the fish a distinctive undulating movement that one can easily learn to recognize, even at a distance. The most distinctive members, and at the same time fair representatives of the immense variety of the family, are the cleaner wrasse (Labroides dimidiatus), with dark-blue and black horizontal bands; these fish are incessantly occupied in cleaning other fish of parasites and organic residue,

and the huge humphead wrasse (Cheilinus undulatus) can grow to lengths of up to two meters. All of the Labridae are decidedly diurnal, and it is therefore impossible to see them swim at night. With some patience and care, however, it is possible to find them in their night-time hiding places, as they sleep half-buried in the sand or lying on one side in the shelter of a rock or a grotto, or else wrapped in a capsule of mucous, like that used by the parrotfish. Moreover, many of them change color, taking on drabber and less flashy colorings. And for that matter, variations in color are one of the distinctive characteristics of the Labridae, and many species change color sharply when, in the process of maturing, they change sex from female to male.

69 top
*Sling-jaw wrasse
female*
(Epibulus
insidiator).

69 bottom
Moon wrasse
(Thalassoma
lunare).

68-69
Humphead wrasse
(Cheilinus
undulatus)
and shark sucker
(Echeneis
naucrates).

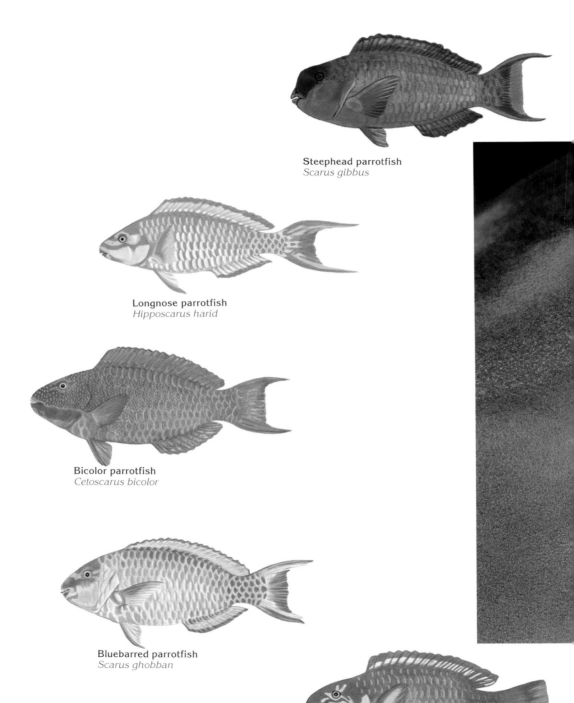

Steephead parrotfish
Scarus gibbus

Longnose parrotfish
Hipposcarus harid

Bicolor parrotfish
Cetoscarus bicolor

Bluebarred parrotfish
Scarus ghobban

Bullethead parrotfish
Scarus sordidus

Rusty parrotfish
Scarus ferrugineus

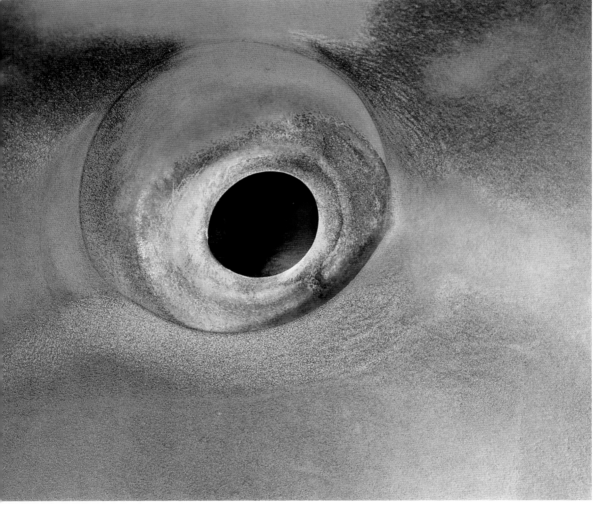

70-71 *Detail of a parrotfish's eye* (Scarus sp.).

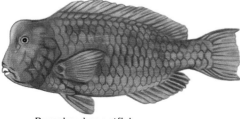

Bumphead parrotfish
Bolbometopon muricatum

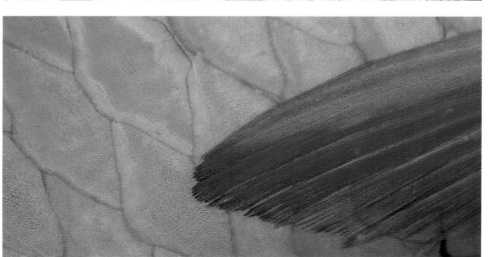

72 top and 72-73
Rusty parrotfish
(Scarus
ferrugineus).

72 center
Steephead
parrotfish
(Scarus gibbus).

72 bottom
Detail of
parrotfish's scales.

As any scuba diver soon discovers, the underwater world is anything but silent. Creaking noises, whistles, and thumping roars are common sounds under the surface, but the most easily recognizable of them all are the sharp cracks produced by the Scaridae or parrotfish as they tear away at the coral with their powerful beaks. Exceedingly colorful and perhaps far more changeable than the Labridae, since their colorings can change with age, gender, and season of the year, the Scaridae have powerful bodies, flattened sidewise, covered with large scales. More than by these characteristics, however, the parrotfish (genera *Scarus*, *Bolbometopon*, etc.) can be easily recognized by their mouths, featuring large and prominent teeth that have been transformed into dental plates in the form of a beak, perfectly suited to breaking away pieces of coral; the parrotfish in fact feed on polyps. At regular intervals, then, it is possible to observe around the parrotfish the sudden blossoming of a little white cloud, which quickly dissolves. The cloud consists of the undigested remains of the coral, ground up and transformed into a very fine coral sand. Like the Labridae, the Scaridae too are diurnal fish.

At sunset, each specimen takes refuge in its den or hideaway, and begins to secrete a transparent mucous covering, a sort of cocoon that entirely envelopes the fish, and dissolves the following day. The function of this covering (which not all Scaridae possess) is believed to be that of preventing nocturnal predators from discovering the sleeping parrotfish by their sense of smell.

SURGEONFISH

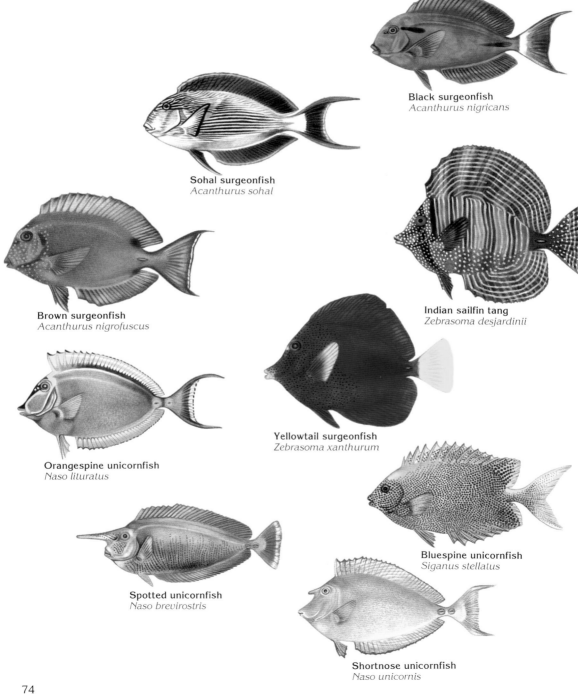

Black surgeonfish
Acanthurus nigricans

Sohal surgeonfish
Acanthurus sohal

Indian sailfin tang
Zebrasoma desjardinii

Brown surgeonfish
Acanthurus nigrofuscus

Orangespine unicornfish
Naso lituratus

Yellowtail surgeonfish
Zebrasoma xanthurum

Bluespine unicornfish
Siganus stellatus

Spotted unicornfish
Naso brevirostris

Shortnose unicornfish
Naso unicornis

Oval in shape, with broad dorsal and anal fins, and with tails that are often sickle-shaped, with elongated lobes, the Acanthuridae, or surgeonfish are quite common in the central reef area, where the lighting is brightest and where the algae eaten by these fishes grow most abundantly. One distinctive characteristic shared by all surgeonfish, and which has given the group its strange name, is the presence of remarkably sharp spines, as sharp as a scalpel, set along the sides of the caudal peduncle. Observing the peduncle with particular care one can make out an area of contrasting color with sharp spines generally movable, which can be raised in self-defense all pointing forward. In general, they are used to settle territorial disputes, but more as a method of intimidation and threat than as an actual weapon. These spines also pose a potential danger for humans, and it is best to keep this in mind in the presence of large schools of Acanthuridae.

75 top
Sohal surgeonfish
(Acanthurus sohal).

75 centre
Blacktongue
unicornfish
(Naso hexacanthus).

75 bottom·
Bluespine unicornfish
(Naso unicornis).

*T*RIGGERFISH AND OTHER ODDITIES

Titan triggerfish
Balistoides viridescens

Yellowmargin triggerfish
Pseudobalistes flavimarginatus

Picasso triggerfish
Rhinecanthus assasi

Blackspotted pufferfish
Arothron stellatus

Blue triggerfish
Pseudobalistes fuscus

Cube boxfish
Ostracion cubicus

Harlequin filefish
Oxymonacanthus halli

Orangestriped triggerfish
Balistapus undulatus

Redtooth triggerfish
Odonus niger

76-77
Yellowspotted
burrfish
(Chilomycterus
spilostylus).

Pearl toby pufferfish
Canthigaster margaritata

Burrfish
Diodon hystrix

Large, slightly flattened on the sides, and covered with small but extremely strong bony plates, the triggerfish (Balistidae) are distinguished by two dorsal fins.
The first of these fins gave the fish their name, as it is made up of three rays that can be intertwined with a triggering mechanism that locks the longest ray into place. This mechanism goes into operation when a triggerfish takes shelter in a grotto or fissure, locking it into place so that it becomes impossible to extract it from its lair. Another notable characteristic of the triggerfish consists of its dentition, equipped with powerful chisel-teeth, fastened solidly to jaws moved by particularly powerful muscles, with which these fish can easily crush the shells of the crustaceans, molluscs, and sea urchins on which they feed. They use a remarkable technique to catch sea urchins. Fearful of the sharp spines with which the sea urchins defend themselves, the triggerfish may seize two of the spines, and with them drag the sea urchin upward, release it, and then attack it from its unprotected lower side as it drops slowly through the water; they also direct powerful jets of water at the base of the sea urchin to overturn it for the same purpose. The triggerfish, lastly, are very territorial and it is advisable to keep a safe distance to avoid being attacked, especially when they are guarding their nests.

78-79
Orangestripped
triggerfish
(Balistapus
undulatus).

79 top
Titan triggerfish
(Balistoides
viridescens).

79 bottom
Redtooth
triggerfish
(Odonus niger).

Powerful teeth are also distinctive characteristics of globefish, porcupinefish, and boxfish (Ostraciidae). The latter have a rigid body, made up of bony plates that are often hexagonal, from which tiny fins project, their swirling motion moving these rigid fish through the corals like tiny helicopters. The globefish (Tetraodontidae) and porcupinefish (Diodontidae), on the other hand, share the ability to inflate themselves when threatened. This feature, which always interests and attracts divers, is exhausting for the fish; therefore, one should not touch them or attempt to provoke them into inflating themselves, as this will exhaust and cause them harm.

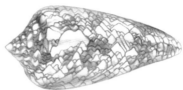

Cone shell
Conus textile

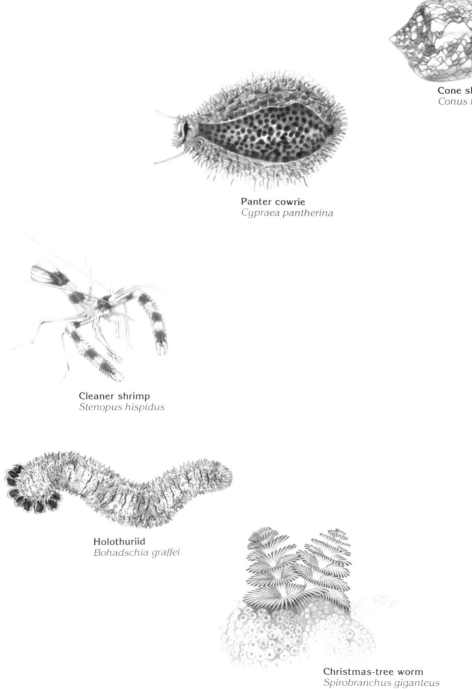

Panter cowrie
Cypraea pantherina

Cleaner shrimp
Stenopus hispidus

Holothuriid
Bohadschia graffei

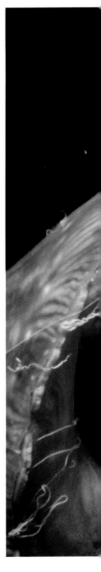

Christmas-tree worm
Spirobranchus giganteus

Pin-cushion starfish
Choriaster granulosus

Pin-cushion urchin
Asthenosoma varium

Starfish
Fromia sp.

83 Ermit crab
(Dardanus sp.).

Extremely common, as well, are the mollusks and echinoderms. Among the mollusks, there are at least three species that can be considered emblematic of these sea beds: the Spanish dancer *(Hexabranchus sanguineus)*, the triton *(Charonia tritonis)*, and the clam (*Tridacna maxima*). The first-named species is the largest and most spectacular nudibranch to be found in the Red Sea; in some areas it can attain a length of as much as 40 centimeters. Reddish in color, with white edges and large feathery gills, this nudibranch — with the delicacy of its movements — can capture the imagination of anyone having the good fortune to see and watch it swim through the water. Equally large is the triton, the chief predator of the crown of thorns starfish *(Acanthaster planci)*, which can destroy in a very brief time as much as a square meter of coral reef.

Clams are too well known to be described, though we need to point out that their reputation as traps for scuba divers is quite exaggerated. Certainly, if they are touched, they do react by closing their valves, but the movement involved is so slow that anyone would have time to avoid being caught.

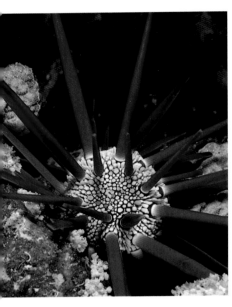

Among the Echinoderms, the sea urchin is the best known but also the most dangerous. Alongside the innocuous pencil urchin, which by day remain hidden in the fissures, and the sand dollars, buried in the bottom silt, there are at least two other species that is worthwhile to learn to recognize: the diadema urchin *(Diadema setosum)* and the pincushion urchin *(Asthenosoma varium)*.

The former has exceedingly long spines, as thin as glass needles, which break at the slightest impact. Coated with poison, they can cause painful wounds. Oddly enough, this sea urchin is endowed with sensitive cells that are similar to eyes. It is enough to cast a shadow on one of these creatures to see it react, orienting all its spines immediately in one's direction. Apparently more harmless, with its reddish color upon which rounded white formations stand out, is the pincushion urchin.

Actually, however, the white formations hide a dangerous feature, as they are packed with poison and connected to sharp spines.

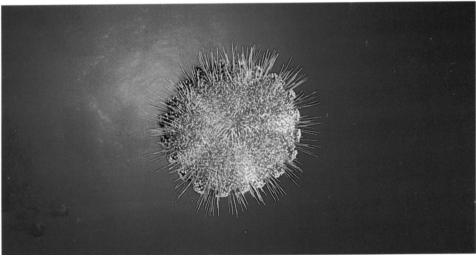

86 top
Slate pencil urchin
(Heterocentratus
mammilatus).

86 center and
bottom
Pincushion urchin
(Asthenosoma
varium).

87 Starfish
(Fromia sp.).

Quite common, especially where constant currents prevail, are the other Echinoderms, such as the Crinoids or the sea lilies, with their numerous feathery arms spreading out from a small body that remains fastened to corals or to gorgonians through articulated, prehensile tentacles. Lastly, we cannot overlook the crustaceans. Lobsters, crayfish, crabs, and hermit crabs move to and fro across the sea bed, especially by night, working as efficient and thorough scavengers. Some of them, on the other hand, establish relationships of close-linked symbiosis with larger animals (sea anemones and fish), cleaning them of parasites and organic residue in exchange for protection and food. In general, these species are smaller, and it takes some practice to see them, but real diving means paying attention even to the smallest organisms.

88 top
Feather stars
(Heterometra sp.).

88 bottom left
Mimetic
spider crab
(Majidae fam.).

88 bottom right
Humpbacked
shrimps
(Hyppoliysmata
grabham).

89 Cleaner shrimp
(Periclimenes sp.).

THE REEF BUILDERS

Mountain coral
Porites sp.

Rose coral
Lobophyllya sp.

Mushroom coral
Fungia sp.

Brain coral
Platygyra sp.

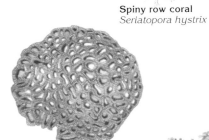

Honeycomb coral
Favites sp.

Spiny row coral
Seriatopora hystrix

Soft coral
Dendroneph

Red cave coral
Tubastrea sp.

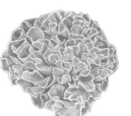

Serpentine salad coral
Turbinaria mesenterina

Staghorn coral
Acropora sp.

90-91
Jewel fairy basslet
(Pseudanthias
squamipinnis)
*swim amidst soft
corals*
(Dendronephthya
sp.).

Leafy coral
Pachyseris sp.

Sea fan
Subergorgia hicksoni

Fire coral
Millepora dichotoma

Raspberry coral
Pocillopora sp.

Even more complex and varied than the world of the fish is the universe of the invertebrates, which dominates in terms of numbers the floor of the Red Sea. The coral reefs built by the incessant and slow activity of dozens of different species of corals are the very foundation of underwater life. Encouraged by crystal-clear waters, warm and rich in nutrition, the tiny polyps that make up the colonies of the Acropora or the Madreporarians multiply, synthesize calcium carbonate from sea water, and erect fantastic constructions, in an apparent chaos that actually meets exceedingly precise ecological requirements.

92-93 Detail of the tips of branches of coral. (Acropora sp.).

93 top Fire corals (Millepora dichotoma).

93 bottom Distinctive picture of the Red Sea with hard and soft coral formations (Sarcophyton sp.).

For one species, light may be the limiting factor; for other species it may be the degree of exposure to the wave action or to the currents that limits growth. The apparent similarity to petrified trees and bushes, or in some cases to large rocks, should not fool the diver. Though the polyps may be tiny and almost invisible, or else visible only by night, they are the fundamental component of the coral, from which they extend their tentacles into the water in a continual search for food. Easier to observe are the very colorful soft corals, similar in appearance to little translucent trees, which expand by night in luxuriant forms to intercept with greater efficiency the clouds of plankton that sweep by on the currents. Without a rigid skeleton, and therefore described as soft, the Alcyonarians are most common in the upper 15 meters from the surface, where there are many species — more or less encrusting — that at first glance look like large sea anemones with short but numerous tentacles, or formations of moss, in some cases covering many square meters of sea floor. Also very common are the gorgonians, generally quite similar to those found on the floor of the Mediterranean, but in some cases quite different, and capable of taking on a threadlike shape, straight, with a slight spiralling bend, or with a terminal curl, that distinguishes this creature from the so-called whip corals.

94 top
A group of tubular sponges (Siphonochelina sp.).

94 center left
A series of encrusting Anthozoa with expanded tentacles.

94 center right
An expanded polyp of Tubastrea.

94 bottom left
A colony of gorgonians (fam. Plexauridae) offers support to a number of crinoids.

95 A giant gorgonian sea fan (Subergorgia hicksoni).

96 A distintive black coral spiral (Cirripathes sp.).

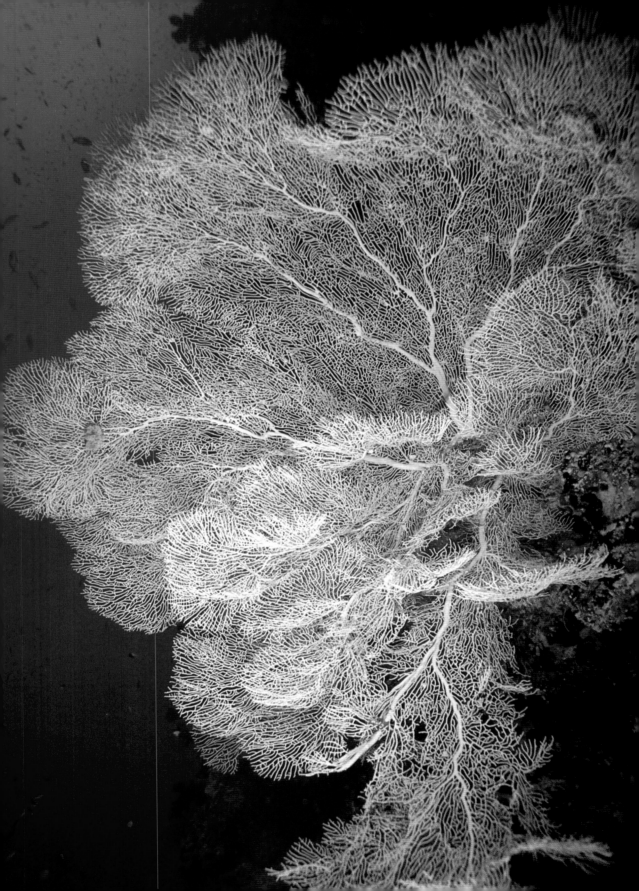

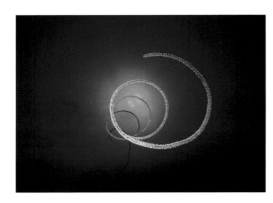